TABLE OF

Needham, Massachussetts
Upper Saddle River, New Jersey

Copyright © 2005 by Pearson Education, Inc., publishing as Pearson Prentice Hall, Upper Saddle River, New Jersey 07458. All rights reserved. Printed in the United States of America. This publication is protected by copyright, and permission should be obtained from the publisher prior to any prohibited reproduction, storage in a retrieval system, or transmission in any form or by any means, electronic, mechanical, photocopying, recording, or likewise. The publisher hereby grants permission to reproduce these pages, in part or in whole, for classroom use only, the number not to exceed the number of students in each class. Notice of copyright must appear on all copies. For information regarding permission(s), write to: Rights and Permissions Department.

Pearson Prentice Hall™ is a trademark of Pearson Education, Inc.
Pearson® is a registered trademark of Pearson plc.
Prentice Hall® is a registered trademark of Pearson Education, Inc.

ISBN 0-13-128428-2

2 3 4 5 6 7 8 9 10   08 07 06 05 04

Redefining Assessment
by Heidi Hayes Jacobs, Ed.D.

The operational definition of "assessment" has changed dramatically over the last ten years, and this change is revolutionizing teaching. Basically, assessment is simply evidence—evidence of a student's growth or regression. The only way a teacher knows whether learning has occurred is by looking at the student's performance.

Teachers gather many kinds of evidence. A primary source of evidence is standardized testing. Student performance assessment is important as well. It is tempting for teachers to pit one type of assessment against the other. This would be a mistake, however, for each is useful in its own way. Ultimately, we need to redefine assessment to become more comprehensive. We need a wider range of revealing evidence.

Standardized Testing

Standardized testing is helpful for diagnosing a student's ability to perform a skill or recall information. Standardized testing is limited when gathering evidence of a student's ability to use or apply these skills and knowledge in the context of "real life" problem-solving. In other words, standardized testing is of limited use when assessing students' reasoning, composition, and evaluative skills. If the ability to compose a well-reasoned point of view is being assessed, a traditional standardized test cannot provide that information. If the ability to select from four choices the appropriate verb to agree with a subject is being assessed, then a standardized test is quite useful. Standardized tests are diagnostic tools for specific competencies.

Standardized testing is changing. For example, electronic portfolios will eventually replace the way students submit applications for college admission. In the future, students will provide to colleges, either on a disk or through electronic mail, a portfolio of work samples. These work samples will be used, in combination with SAT scores, to determine the student's eligibility for admission. Most testing agencies expect that more writing samples will be required on standardized testing. When parents question teachers about how new forms of assessment will affect their child's chances of being adequately prepared for college, the teacher can answer that by using both standardized testing and student performance assessment, your school is anticipating future trends in the college admissions process. Certainly those students looking to join the work force after high school graduation most likely will be hired based on demonstrated performance as exemplified in school-to-work programs.

Student Performance Assessment

Student performance assessment answers the need for a greater range of data on which to gauge student progress. Comprehensive assessment gives teachers, admissions counselors, and other educators more evidence—and more valid evidence—on which to base their analysis of each student. Students must be able to do more than *study* a particular subject; they must be able to *apply* that information to any number of situations. When they can do so, teachers can evaluate their performance more accurately.

How does a basketball coach know that his or her players are "learning basketball"? He or she watches the players in drills. The coach also uses structured practices and controlled "rehearsals" or scrimmages. But the real test of the players' ability comes when they are faced with an opposing team whose strategies and plays are a mystery. In short, the students are basketball players. Similarly, as a history teacher, you do not want students simply to study or read about history. You want them to be historians. You don't want students to simply study math, but to be mathematicians. That is what we are looking for in performance assessment—not simply studying the text, but actually playing the game.

Feedback Systems for Students

Even when students are allowed to "play the game," the only way that their work will improve is if they "self-assess" that work. When students are asked what constitutes a good essay, or a good historical analysis, they often do not know the answer. This is because they have learned not what constitutes quality, but rather what to do to get an "A" from a specific teacher. They haven't internalized what is considered good work. How can students improve if they do not know what quality looks like?

Rubrics

The answer to this dilemma is to design a rubric with your students. A rubric is not a grading system. It is a

 © Pearson Education, Inc.

The Specific Criteria for Assessment Each criterion in the rubric should indicate a specific aspect or quality to be focused on or assessed in the product or performance. Although there may be multiple criteria included in a rubric, teachers or students may focus instruction on only one of the criteria at a time. Criteria may also vary depending on the stage of the project; for example, the criteria for a first draft are very different from those for a final draft.

Indicators Indicators must be descriptive and nonjudgmental. Do not use words such as "excellent" or "poor"— rather, the task is to describe what excellence looks like in a product or performance for any one criterion.

The Standards or Levels of Excellence These should be in terms that are readily understandable to the student. An even number of levels should always be used because it forces judgment. With an odd number there is a tendency to "clump" in the middle of the scale and avoid judgment. The levels can be represented by words, numbers, or letter grades.

Graphing Data Rubric

	Distinguished	Proficient	Limited	Attempted
Choice of Format and Axes	Graph format illustrates data perfectly; each axis measures appropriate data	Graph format illustrates data adequately; each axis measures appropriate data	Graph format not well chosen; axes measure correct data but are switched	Graph format is inappropriate and does not illustrate data; axes do not measure appropriate data
Scale and Sequence	Scale consistent and accurate; very appropriate for subject matter; all points in sequence with care taken on placement within increments	Scale consistent, accurate, and appropriate; items in sequence; increments marked	Scale roughly drawn; a few items out of sequence; increments marked	No apparent scale; numerous items out of sequence; increments not marked
Mechanics	Flawless	Few mechanical errors	Some errors in spelling, identification, or labeling	Many errors in spelling, identification, or labelings
Presentation	Visually striking; attention apparent to making graph an effective tool for communicating information	Clear, uncluttered, and attractive	Legible but somewhat cluttered	Illegible or messy

lesson in what constitutes quality. It is a declaration of expectations and a means of self-assessment for the student. Students are more likely to be able to perform well if they know what constitutes quality performance. When designing rubrics, teachers and students should incorporate the following elements:

- the standards or levels of excellence
- the specific criteria for assessment
- the specific indicators describing what the various levels of excellence look like for each of the criteria.

Students can use the rubric to edit and analyze their own work. When a teacher reads a paper and marks it up in "red," the teacher is the editor. Instead, the teacher should call attention to problems or issues, give the work back to the students, and let them become the editors. If the learners do not know how to follow through on revision, the teacher's job is to teach them how to edit—not to edit for them. When this type of self-assessment is used consistently, teachers see students begin to evaluate and value the quality of their own work. They begin to understand what areas they need to work on in order to improve. The revision and editing process is not only true for written products, but for visual and oral performances as well.

Rubrics are particularly effective when used across grades and between levels. In such situations, rubrics help teachers know what students have focused on in earlier grades so that they can build on that knowledge, not repeat information, and not assume knowledge that does not yet exist.

Some Cautions

An important point to remember when using rubrics and student performance assessment is that the standards stay constant. Tasks will change, but the standards should not. A common tendency is for teachers to respond to areas of student weakness by lowering standards. Students do not benefit from this lowering of standards. Clear, high, and consistent standards raise the level of student performance. The teacher's work is to assist students on skills to raise the quality of their work. A struggling student may need a task broken into

© Pearson Education, Inc.

parts or a simpler task, but quality will not be changeable. By the same token, a student showing excellent performance may need a more challenging task. In both instances, the standards are constant.

Another potential pitfall occurs when teachers attempt to use feedback mechanisms such as rubrics to categorize students into a holistic "level" or "stage." Such categorization is limited and misleading because students may be at varying levels with different criteria on one project. If such categorization is used, teachers are in fact falling back on the old "A," "B," "C" method of grading, with teacher comments such as "good work," "nice word choice"—which is of limited value to students. With the new method of grading, the student reflects on what the grade actually means, monitors his or her performance, and takes action to do progressively better. The rubric translates the grading system into a meaningful feedback system. Presently, most grades are an indication of the individual teacher's values. If a high school student has eight teachers in a day, he or she has eight different grading standards.

Active Learning

To make use of student performance assessment, the teacher must reevaluate his or her role in the classroom. One positive change that teachers notice is that they spend less time reading papers and assignments. Instead of reviewing and editing a student's first draft, the teacher will spend his or her time up front, defining and clarifying expectations and levels of excellence. This does not mean that teachers no longer read students' papers. It is simply that the quality of those papers will be higher when they first come to the teacher. The burden shifts from teacher to student to self-assess his or her performance and make adjustments. The teacher's job is to take the evidence present in the student's work and help him or her figure out ways to improve that work.

Teachers will find student performance assessment to be more efficient than old ways of assessment. Students will receive more consistent feedback, and as a consequence, their work will improve. In the past, teachers have taken on much of the burden of performing for students when in fact, it is the students who need to perform and practice. It does little good for the coach to play basketball while the team watches. Similarly, it is of little use for the history teacher to analyze a historical event on the board while the class watches. When the purpose of the practice is clear to students, there is less resistance. Students practice basketball or music because they can see the purpose of that practice and they can see the results when they do not practice. This habit of mind changes the role of student to become a self-assessor and self-teacher. It is an attitude and approach that must be cultivated in all areas of the curriculum. Student performance assessment will help students understand the value of their work and support lifelong learning.

Sample Rubrics

Most of the assessment tools included in this folder appear in two different formats—as completed rubrics and as evaluation forms. The first format, the rubric, includes the standards of excellence across the top, the specific criteria for assessment along the left side, and the indicators filled in within the chart. These "completed" rubrics can be used in several ways. First, they are meant to be shared with students at the beginning of an assignment so that students are aware of what constitutes good work. Second, they can be used by students evaluating their own or each other's work (either focusing on one particular criterion at a time or on all the criteria).

Each rubric has also been included in a second format—an evaluation form. Teachers and students can use these forms to indicate which level of work (standard of excellence) was achieved for each of the criteria. The space within the chart and at the bottom of the form can be used to make note of specific examples or to provide comments. Finally, teachers are encouraged to use these rubrics as starting points for developing their own rubrics. Each section of *Magruder's American Government* Teacher's Edition has a lesson plan and a number of classroom activities. You can use the assessment rubrics in this booklet to assess those activities.

Dr. Heidi Hayes Jacobs is president of Curriculum Designers, Inc. and has served as an educational consultant to thousands of schools nationally and internationally. She served as an adjunct associate professor in the Department of Curriculum and Teaching at Teacher's College, Columbia University, New York City. She works with schools and K-12 districts on issues pertaining to curricular reform, instructional strategies to encourage critical thinking, and strategic planning. Her books, *Interdisciplinary Curriculum: Design and Implementation* and *Mapping the Big Picture: Integrating Curriculum and Assessment K-12*, both published by ASCD, are bestsellers. The fundamental backbone of her experience comes from her years as a teacher of high school, junior high school, and elementary children in Utah, Massachusetts, and New York.

© Pearson Education, Inc.

Study Skills Activity

Note Taking and Outlining

DIRECTIONS
Read the passages below and then complete the outline as indicated.

You might groan at the idea of taking notes while in class or as you read your textbook, but relax! Notes are valuable and they make your job easier, not harder. Why? Because you will learn to study from your notes and improve your test scores.

✎ Goodbye to Rereading

Many students try to reread chapters the night before a test. But rereading is probably the hardest and least efficient way to study. Even if you do reread the chapters, the information will not be organized in a way that will help you to remember it.

Note taking keeps you alert. It helps you to interact with the ideas you are trying to remember. The result is better understanding—and better test results.

✎ Hello to Outlining

One of the best ways to take notes is in the form of an outline. Outlining helps you think in a more organized way. It gives you an early start on studying. It also gives you a head start on preparing essays, reports, and projects. So, how do you go about outlining? The easiest form of outlining is the modified outline.

✎ The Modified Outline

An outline groups related information under major category headings. For practice in outlining, look at one of the chapters in your textbook and complete an outline similar to the one on this page. You will need to modify this outline to fit the number of sections and headings in your chapter. You can also use a modified outline format to record the main ideas of a discussion or of your teacher's lecture.

© Pearson Education, Inc.

Chapter Title_____

I. Section 1 Title_____

   A. First Section Heading _____

      1. Main Idea _____

      2. Main Idea _____

   B. Second Section Heading _____

      1. Main Idea _____

      2. Main Idea _____

   C. Third Section Heading _____

      1. Main Idea _____

      2. Main Idea _____

II. Section 2 Title_____

   A. First Section Heading_____

      1. Main Idea _____

      2. Main Idea _____

   B. Second Section Heading _____

      1. Main Idea _____

      2. Main Idea _____

   C. Third Section Heading _____

      1. Main Idea _____

      2. Main Idea _____

Study Skills Activity
Studying with SQ3R

DIRECTIONS

Reading a textbook is different from reading a novel or a play or a newspaper. Textbooks are organized to help you find and use information quickly and easily. Take advantage of their organization. One method to use is SQ3R: Survey, Question, Read, Recite, and Review. To use this method, follow the steps below using a chapter from your textbook.

✎ Survey

Before you start to read, look over the pages in the chapter.

1. Read the chapter title. It tells you in a few words what your reading will be about. It also gives you information about the main idea of the chapter.
2. Read the titles of the sections in the chapter. Ask yourself how these titles relate to the chapter title.
3. Look at the beginning of each section. Each section begins with a reading preview. It may include vocabulary words and main ideas that are covered in the section.
4. Look at the illustrations and captions to get a better idea of the reading.
5. Read any introductory materials.

✎ Question

Starting with the first section of the chapter, write a question for each subheading in the section. Begin your questions with words like how, what, why, when, and who. Write your questions on a separate sheet of paper.

✎ Read

Read the section. Now, you are reading with a purpose—you are looking for the answers to the questions you have made up.

✎ Recite

Ask yourself the questions and recite the answers without looking back at the reading. Then write the answer to each question so that you will have notes to study. Don't forget to check your answers against each section. These notes will come in handy as you prepare for your test.

✎ Review

Go over your questions later to make sure that you can still recall the answers. Recall questions are a common part of many tests. If necessary, use your notes for help. Review the questions the following day, and again in a week. If you review regularly, you will probably remember the material for a long time.

© Pearson Education, Inc.

Study Skills Activity
Concentrating

© Pearson Education, Inc.

DIRECTIONS

If you have problems concentrating, you need to identify the kinds of things that distract you. Examples of some of the things that might distract you are listed below.

Use the boxes beside each type of distraction to check off those that apply to you, and add any others that are relevant. Study the suggested solutions. Then, use the questions that follow to prepare your own action plan for overcoming distractions.

Distractions	Possible Solutions
❏ Noise	Turn off the radio and television. Ask to be left alone while you are studying.
❏ No place to study	Use the library, or find a quiet corner at home.
❏ Telephone interruptions	Ask friends not to call during certain hours.
❏ Missing materials	Check to make sure you have all you need before you start.
❏ Too much on your mind	Make a list, and figure out priorities.
❏ Bad attitude toward studying	Keep your eye on your goals. Talk with someone about the value of education.
❏ Emotional problems	Seek help. Take action to plan your personal life.
❏ Too focused on personal life	Set aside other times to plan your personal life.
❏ Too tired to study	Figure out how to get more sleep.
❏ Lacking energy	Start a regular exercise program to build your reserve of energy. Eat a balanced diet on a regular schedule.
❏ Other	
❏ Other	

1. Which of the distractions you have checked above do you need to deal with first? What can you do about it?

2. Which distraction do you plan to deal with next? What can you do about it?

3. Who can you ask to help you overcome your distractions?

4. What other actions can you take to help you concentrate more effectively on studying?

Study Skills Activity
Improving Your Memory

© Pearson Education, Inc.

DIRECTIONS

Much of your schoolwork involves remembering information you have heard or read. Four rules for improving your memory are described below. Study the four rules, and then answer the questions that follow on a separate sheet of paper.

Rule 1   Use what you want to remember as soon as you can.

For example, when you are introduced to someone, you are more likely to remember the person's name if you repeat it as you shake hands with the person.

1. How can you use this rule to help you remember the names of the key places or people you are studying?

Rule 2   Use the "Association Method" to remember.

Try and associate something with names and ideas that you learn. To remember that the Supreme Court interprets the Constitution, note that Court and Constitution begin with the same letters.

2. What associations can you devise to help you remember the facts below?
    a. The Constitution became effective in 1789.
    b. The Speaker of the House is second in the line of presidential succession.
    c. The Federal Communications Commission is an independent regulatory commission.

Rule 3   Use the "Link Method" to remember.

Suppose you want to remember a list of the tools that geographers use in their research: remote satellite images, censuses, globes, and maps. Try creating a mental picture of a geographer standing next to a huge globe that has a satellite circling it, and the geographer is attempting to take a census of the people drawn on the globe. It doesn't matter if the picture in your mind is ridiculous, as long as it helps you remember.

3. What picture can you visualize that will help you remember that the United States has a two-party system?

Rule 4   Use acronyms and acrostics.

Acronyms and acrostics are simple ways to remember details. You can create a word (acronym) or a sentence (acrostic) made from the first letter of each item you want to remember.

4. Make up an acrostic that will help you remember the three major economic systems: capitalism, communism, and socialism.

Study Skills Activity
How to Prepare for a Test

© Pearson Education, Inc.

DIRECTIONS

Preparing for a test calls for long-range planning, short-range planning, and planning for the test time itself. By paying attention to each aspect of test preparation, you can greatly improve your chances of doing well on the test. Read the guidelines for each phase and answer the questions.

✎ Long-Range Planning

- Give yourself plenty of time to prepare for the test. Don't leave everything until the night before the test.
- Set aside blocks of uninterrupted time for studying, with short breaks at regular intervals.

   1. Based on your experience in the past, what changes do you need to make to the way you study for a test so that your long-range planning will be better next time?

✎ Short-Range Planning

- If you prepared in advance, do something relaxing on the night before the test.
- Get a good night's sleep before the test.
- Eat a nutritious meal before the test.
- Wear comfortable clothing on the day of the test. If possible, wear a watch during the test or sit where you can see a clock.
- Make sure you have all the materials you need to take the test. Find out if you need a certain type of pencil, for example, and bring several with you. Sharpen them beforehand.
- Be sure you know where the test is being given and at what time. Plan to arrive early.

   2. Based on your experience of tests in the past, what changes do you need to make to your short-range planning?

   3. On a separate sheet, write a list of the things you need to do during the 24 hours before your next test. Place the sheet in a safe place so that you can refer to it when you need to.

✎ During the Test

- Read the directions carefully.
- Read each question carefully.
- Answer the "easy" questions first. Then, go back to the ones that will take more time.

   4. Based on your past experience of tests, which kinds of questions caused you the greatest difficulty?

   5. What can you do now to prevent those difficulties in the future?

Writing Assignment Rubric

		Distinguished	Proficient	Limited	Unsatisfactory
CONTENT					
	Introduction	Attitude is defined; thesis is clearly focused; subject is significant	Thesis is clear; provides direction for essay	Unclear; formulaic; not creative	Introduction is incomplete, ineffective, or missing
	Idea Development	Interesting; sophisticated; insightful	Clear and thoughtful	Simplistic; uneven in quality; lacking in relevance	Absent or ineffective
	Support or Evidence	Detailed; accurate; convincing	Sufficient and accurate	Uneven	Vague, missing, or inaccurate
	Word Choice	Engaging and powerful choice of words	Appropriate to task	Uneven	Limited, monotonous, or inappropriate
	Conclusion	Extends; connects; comments on topics	Purposeful and perceptive	Summarizes previously stated information	Absent, incomplete, or unfocused
ORGANIZATION					
	Topic Sentences	Clearly related to thesis; comprehensive; incorporates effective transitions	Comprehensive and logical	Provides bland restatement of thesis; narrow or inaccurate	Absent
	Paragraph Order	Contributes to an effective argument; reinforces the content	Demonstrates a clear plan	Ineffective or inconsistent	Random
	Transitions	Effective and varied	Clear and functional	Mechanical	Absent
MECHANICS					
	Sentence Structure	Complete; varied; interesting	Complete and correct	Variety is present; some errors are evident	Repetitious; fragments and run-ons are frequent
	Punctuation/Spelling	Error-free	Errors present but do not interfere with meaning	Careless or distracting	Block meaning
	Voice	Distinctive; appropriate to task and audience	Clear and authentic	Mechanical; formulaic	Unclear

© Pearson Education, Inc.

Writing Assignment Evaluation Form

© Pearson Education, Inc.

	Distinguished	Proficient	Limited	Unsatisfactory
CONTENT				
Introduction				
Idea Development				
Support or Evidence				
Word Choice				
Conclusion				
ORGANIZATION				
Topic Sentences				
Paragraph Order				
Transitions				
MECHANICS				
Sentence Structure				
Punctuation/Spelling				
Voice				

COMMENTS:

Position Paper Rubric

	Exceptional	Admirable	Acceptable	Attempted
Idea Development	Takes a strong, well defined position; uses at least four appropriate reasons with at least three supporting details for each reason	Clear position taken and defined; some reasons and some details present but not fully developed	Position is not clearly stated; development is brief, unrelated, unsupported general statements, reasons, and details; minimal facts used	No clear position taken; undeveloped reasons; no facts used
Organization	Writer demonstrates logical, subtle sequencing of ideas through well-developed paragraphs; transitions are used to enhance organization; a gripping introduction and a strong conclusion evident	Paragraph development present but not perfected	Logical organization; organization of ideas not fully developed; introduction and conclusion present but not fully developed	No evidence of paragraph structure; no introduction or conclusion; illogical organization of ideas
Use of Resources	Uses appropriate information from all subject areas to support position; uses additional resources to develop position; uses a range of primary and secondary sources (six or more)	Demonstration of knowledge of multiple subject areas; use of four resources	Little use of knowledge of multiple subject areas; uses less than four resources	No evidence of subject matter or resources used
Management of Time	Submitted on time; utilizes class time appropriately; seeks help in research and writing; evidence of homework each night; student-designed action plan	Utilizes class time; deadlines met; submitted on time	Deadlines met with supervision; home preparation minimal	Consistently unprepared; late; unfinished; no evidence of homework
Mechanics and Language Usage	Error-free paper, accurate spelling and punctuation, capitalization, and usage; variety of sentence structures, rich vocabulary	Few errors present in spelling, punctuation, capitalization, and usage; some attempt at sentence variety; occasional use of rich vocabulary	Incorrect sentence structure; spelling, punctuation, capitalization errors present; repetitious vocabulary; weak language usage	Multiple errors present in sentence structure, spelling, punctuation, and capitalization; weak vocabulary and incorrect language usage
Presentation	Neatly typed, numbered pages; assembled with care; cover sheet with name, grade, and date; creative ideas present; good graphics	Neatly presented; cover sheet complete with attention to aesthetics	Presentation is legible but lacks visual appeal; no cover sheet with name, grade, and date	Difficult to read; not assembled with care; lacks cover sheet

© Pearson Education, Inc.

© Pearson Education, Inc.

Position Paper Evaluation Form

	Exceptional	Admirable	Acceptable	Attempted
Idea Development				
Organization				
Use of Resources				
Management of Time				
Mechanics and Language Usage				
Presentation				

COMMENTS:

Analyzing a Primary Source Rubric

	Exemplary	Adequate	Minimal	Attempted
Analysis of Document	Offers in-depth analysis and interpretation of the document; distinguishes between fact and opinion; explores reliability of author; compares and contrasts author's point of view with views of others	Offers accurate analysis of the document	Demonstrates only a minimal understanding of the document	Reiterates one or two facts from the document but does not offer any analysis or interpretation of the document
Knowledge of Historical Context	Shows evidence of thorough knowledge of period in which source was written; relates primary source to specific context in which it was written	Uses previous general historical knowledge to examine issues included in the document	Limited use of previous historical knowledge without complete accuracy	Barely indicates any previous historical knowledge
Identification of Key Issues/ Main Points	Identifies the key issues and main points included in the primary source; shows understanding of author's goal(s)	Identifies most but not all of the key issues and main points in the primary source	Describes in general terms one issue or concept included in the primary source	Deals only briefly and vaguely with the key issues and main points in the document
Resources	Uses several outside resources in addition to primary source	Uses one to two outside resources in addition to primary source	Relies heavily on the material/information provided	Relies exclusively on the material/ information provided; no evidence of outside resources
Identification of Literary Devices	Analyzes author's use of literary devices such as repetition, irony, analogy, and sarcasm	Mentions author's use of literary devices but does not develop fully	Mentions author's use of literary devices with no explanation	Does not discuss author's use of literary devices
Understanding of Audience	Shows strong understanding of author's audience	Shows some understanding of author's audience	Shows little understanding of author's audience	Shows no understanding of author's audience

© Pearson Education, Inc.

Analyzing a Primary Source Evaluation Form

© Pearson Education, Inc.

	Exemplary	Adequate	Minimal	Attempted
Analysis of Document				
Knowledge of Historical Context				
Identification of Key Issues/ Main Points				
Resources				
Identification of Literary Devices				
Understanding of Audience				

COMMENTS:

Activity Rubric

	Exemplary	Adequate	Minimal	Attempted
Knowledge of Content	Extensive use of relevant information; included extra research; details selected to support main idea were very appropriate	Consistent use of relevant information; included adequate research; details supported main idea and were accurate	Inconsistent use of relevant information; some information included was not relevant; showed some research; main idea was only partially supported by details; some details were inaccurate	Showed little or no incorporation of information; showed little or no research; main idea was not supported by details; many details were inaccurate
Organization	Extremely well organized; logical format was easy to follow; fully explained and illustrated key ideas	Clear organization; focused on key ideas; adequately explained and illustrated key ideas	Somewhat organized; some ideas were not presented clearly	Confusing; illogical format; several key ideas were missing
Mechanics	Flawless	Few mechanical errors	Some errors in spelling, labeling, or dates	Many errors in spelling, labeling, or dates
Presentation	Striking; communicated information effectively; showed strong understanding of audience	Clear, uncluttered, and attractive; showed some understanding of audience	Information could be understood, but product was not attractive; showed little understanding of audience	Illegible or messy; information presented could not be understood; showed no understanding of audience
Creativity	Put a great deal of creative energy into project; very original	Thoughtful format with many creative touches; somewhat original	Some creative touches, but often formulaic; little originality	Put little creative energy into project; no originality

© Pearson Education, Inc.

© Pearson Education, Inc.

Activity Evaluation Form

	Exemplary	Adequate	Minimal	Attempted
Knowledge of Content				
Organization				
Mechanics				
Presentation				
Creativity				

COMMENTS:

Graphing Data Rubric

	Distinguished	Proficient	Limited	Attempted
Choice of Format and Axes	Graph format illustrates data perfectly; each axis measures appropriate data	Graph format illustrates data adequately; each axis measures appropriate data	Graph format not well chosen; axes measure correct data but are switched	Graph format is inappropriate and does not illustrate data; axes do not measure appropriate data
Scale and Sequence	Scale consistent and accurate; very appropriate for subject matter; all points in sequence with care taken on placement within increments	Scale consistent, accurate, and appropriate; items in sequence; increments marked	Scale roughly drawn; a few items out of sequence; increments marked	No apparent scale; numerous items out of sequence; increments not marked
Mechanics	Flawless	Few mechanical errors	Some errors in spelling, identification, or labeling	Many errors in spelling, identification, or labelings
Presentation	Visually striking; attention apparent to making graph an effective tool for communicating information	Clear, uncluttered, and attractive	Legible but somewhat cluttered	Illegible or messy

© Pearson Education, Inc.

Graphing Data Evaluation Form

	Distinguished	Proficient	Limited	Attempted
Choice of Format and Axes				
Scale and Sequence				
Mechanics				
Presentation				

Cooperative Learning Project Rubric: Process

	Exceptional	Admirable	Acceptable	Amateur
Group Participation	All students enthusiastically participate	At least three quarters of students actively participate	At least one half of students confer or present ideas	Only one or two persons actively participate
Shared Responsibility	Responsibility for task is shared evenly	Responsibility is shared by most group members	Responsibility is shared by one half of the group members	Exclusive reliance on one person
Quality of Interaction	Excellent listening and leadership skills exhibited; students reflect awareness of others' views and opinions in their discussions	Students show adeptness in interacting; lively discussion centers on the task	Some ability to interact; attentive listening; some evidence of discussion or alternatives	Little interaction; very brief conversations; some students were disinterested or distracted
Roles Within Group	Each student assigned a clearly defined role; group members perform roles effectively	Each student assigned a role but roles not clearly defined or consistently adhered to	Students assigned roles but roles were not consistently adhered to	No effort made to assign roles to group members

© Pearson Education, Inc.

Cooperative Learning Project Evaluation Form: Process

© Pearson Education, Inc.

	Exceptional	Admirable	Acceptable	Amateur
Group Participation				
Shared Responsibility				
Quality of Interaction				
Roles Within Group				

COMMENTS:

Cooperative Learning Project Rubric: Outcome or Product

	Exceptional	Admirable	Acceptable	Amateur
Organization	Extremely well organized; logical format that was easy to follow; flowed smoothly from one idea to another and was cleverly conveyed; the organization enhanced the effectiveness of the project	Presented in a thoughtful manner; there were signs of organization and most transitions were easy to follow, but at times ideas were unclear	Somewhat organized; ideas were not presented coherently and transitions were not always smooth, which at times distracted the audience	Choppy and confusing; format was difficult to follow; transitions of ideas were abrupt and seriously distracted the audience
Content Accuracy	Completely accurate; all facts were precise and explicit	Mostly accurate; a few inconsistencies or errors in information	Somewhat accurate; more than a few inconsistencies or errors in information	Completely inaccurate; the facts in this project were misleading to the audience
Research	Went above and beyond to research information; solicited material in addition to what was provided; brought in personal ideas and information to enhance project; utilized more than eight types of resources to make project effective	Did a very good job of researching; utilized materials provided to their full potential; solicited more than six types of resources to enhance project; at times took the initiative to find information outside of school	Used the material provided in an acceptable manner, but did not consult any additional resources	Did not utilize resources effectively; did little or no fact gathering on the topic
Creativity	Was extremely clever and presented with originality; a unique approach that truly enhanced the project	Was clever at times; thoughtfully and uniquely presented	Added a few original touches to enhance the project but did not incorporate them throughout	Little creative energy used during this project; was bland, predictable, and lacked "zip"
Presentation Mechanics	Was engaging, provocative, and captured the interest of the audience and maintained this throughout the entire presentation; great variety of visual aids and multimedia; visual aids were colorful and clear	Was well done and interesting to the audience; was presented in a unique manner and was very well organized; some use of visual aids	Was at times interesting and was presented clearly and precisely; was clever at times and was organized in a logical manner; limited variety of visual aids, which were not colorful or clear	Was not organized effectively; was not easy to follow and did not keep the audience interested; no use of visual aids

© Pearson Education, Inc.

Cooperative Learning Project Evaluation Form: Outcome or Product

© Pearson Education, Inc.

	Exceptional	Admirable	Acceptable	Amateur
Organization				
Content Accuracy				
Research				
Creativity				
Presentation Mechanics				

COMMENTS:

Oral Presentation Rubric

	Exceptional	Admirable	Acceptable	Amateur
Content	An abundance of material clearly related to thesis; points are clearly made and all evidence supports thesis; varied use of materials	Sufficient information that relates to thesis; many good points made but there is an uneven balance and little variation	A great deal of information is not clearly connected to the thesis	Thesis not clear; information included does not support thesis in any way
Coherence and Organization	Thesis is clearly stated and developed; specific examples are appropriate and clearly develop thesis; conclusion is clear; shows control; flows together well; good transitions; succinct but not choppy; well organized	Most information presented in logical sequence; generally very well organized but better transitions from idea to idea and medium to medium needed	Concept and ideas are loosely connected; lacks clear transitions; flow and organization are choppy	Presentation is choppy and disjointed; does not flow; development of thesis is vague; no apparent logical order of presentation
Creativity	Very original presentation of material; uses the unexpected to full advantage; captures audience's attention	Some originality apparent; good variety and blending of materials/media	Little or no variation; material presented with little originality or interpretation	Repetitive with little or no variety; insufficient use of multimedia
Material	Balanced use of multimedia materials; properly used to develop thesis; use of media is varied and appropriate	Use of multimedia not as varied and not as well connected to thesis	Choppy use of multimedia materials; lacks smooth transition from one medium to another; multimedia not clearly connected to thesis	Little or no multimedia used or ineffective use of multimedia; imbalance in use of materials—too much of one, not enough of another
Speaking Skills	Poised, clear articulation; proper volume; steady rate; good posture and eye contact; enthusiasm; confidence	Clear articulation but not as polished	Some mumbling; little eye contact; uneven rate; little or no expression	Inaudible or too loud; no eye contact; rate too slow/fast; speaker seemed uninterested and used monotone
Audience Response	Involved the audience in the presentation; points made in creative way; held the audience's attention throughout	Presented facts with some interesting "twists"; held the audience's attention most of the time	Some related facts but went off topic and lost the audience; mostly presented facts with little or no imagination	Incoherent; audience lost interest and could not determine the point of the presentation
Length of Presentation	Within two minutes of allotted time +/-	Within four minutes of allotted time +/-	Within six minutes of allotted time +/-	Ten or more minutes above or below the allotted time

© Pearson Education, Inc.

Oral Presentation Evaluation Form

© Pearson Education, Inc.

	Exceptional	Admirable	Acceptable	Amateur
Content				
Coherence and Organization				
Creativity				
Material				
Speaking Skills				
Audience Response				
Length of Presentation				

COMMENTS:

Participating in Debates/Class Discussion Rubric

	Exemplary	Effective	Minimal	Unsatisfactory
SUBSTANTIVE				
Statement and Identification of Issues	Accurately states and identifies all the relevant issues	Accurately states and identifies some of the issues	States a relevant factual, ethical, or definitional issue as a question	Does not state any issues
Use of Foundational Knowledge	Accurately expresses relevant foundational knowledge pertaining to all issues raised during the debate	Accurately expresses relevant foundational knowledge pertaining to some issues raised during the debate	Accurately expresses relevant foundational knowledge pertaining to an issue raised by someone else	Does not express any relevant foundational knowledge
Elaboration of Statements	Pursues an issue with several elaborated statements	Pursues an issue with at least one elaborated statement	Elaborates a statement with an explanation, reasons, or evidence	Does not elaborate any issues
Argument by Analogy	Uses extensive analogy to advance the discussion	Uses some analogy to advance the discussion	Uses analogy that does not advance the discussion	Does not use analogy to advance the discussion
PROCEDURAL				
Invitation for Contributions from Others	Engages others in the debate by inviting their comments	Invites comments from others	Invites comments from a single person	Does not invite comments from others
Acknowledgment of Others' Statements	Engages others in the debate by acknowledging their contributions	Acknowledges some of the statements of others	Acknowledges one or two statements of others	Does not acknowledge the statements of others
Challenge of the Accuracy, Logic, Relevance, or Clarity of Statements	Constructively challenges the accuracy, clarity, relevance, or logic of statements made	Responds in a civil manner to a statement made by someone else by challenging its accuracy, clarity, relevance, or logic	Does not challenge the accuracy, clarity, relevance, or logic of statements	Does not challenge the accuracy, clarity, relevance, or logic of statements
Summary of Points of Agreement and Disagreement	Summarizes all points of agreement and disagreement clearly	Summarizes several points of agreement or disagreement clearly	Does not summarize points of agreement or disagreement clearly	Does not summarize points of agreement or disagreement

Adapted from Harris, David E. "Assessing Discussion of Public Issues: A Scoring Guide." In *Handbook on Teaching Social Issues,* edited by Ronald W. Evans and David Warren Saxe. Washington, D.C.: National Council for the Social Studies, 1996.

© Pearson Education, Inc.

© Pearson Education, Inc.

NAME _____ CLASS _____ DATE _____

Participating in Debates/Class Discussion Evaluation Form

	Exemplary	Effective	Minimal	Unsatisfactory
SUBSTANTIVE				
Statement and Identification of Issues				
Use of Foundational Knowledge				
Elaboration of Statements				
Argument by Analogy				
PROCEDURAL				
Invitation for Contributions from Others				
Acknowledgment of Others' Statements				
Challenge of the Accuracy, Logic, Relevance, or Clarity of Statements				
Summary of Points of Agreement and Disagreement				

COMMENTS:

Portfolio Assessment

Use this form to assess the portfolio as a whole. Since individual items in the portfolio have likely already been evaluated, it is important to evaluate the strengths and weaknesses of the entire portfolio and to focus on progress.

	Exceptional	Commendable	Acceptable	Unsatisfactory
Variety	☐	☐	☐	☐
Understanding of the content	☐	☐	☐	☐
Evidence of critical thinking and problem-solving ability	☐	☐	☐	☐
Effectiveness of communication	☐	☐	☐	☐
Evidence of creativity	☐	☐	☐	☐
Knowledge of concepts and topical relationships with other content areas	☐	☐	☐	☐
Overall progress in the course	☐	☐	☐	☐

Comments

_____

_____

_____

_____

_____

_____

_____

_____

_____

_____

_____

_____

© Pearson Education, Inc.

Preparing for Standardized Tests

The following pages contain, in convenient blackline master format, the test preparation questions that appear in the bottom margin of your Teacher's Edition of *Magruder's American Government*. Use these questions to give your students practice with analyzing and interpreting primary and secondary sources.

© Pearson Education, Inc.

Preparing for Standardized Tests

Chapter 1

Preparing for Standardized Tests

Have students read the passages under *Origins of the State* on pp. 7–8 and then answer the question below.

Which two theories might be used to explain the origins of Japan, which has an emperor typically chosen from the same familial lines?

A the force theory and the divine right theory

B the evolutionary theory and the force theory

C the social contract theory and the divine right theory

D the evolutionary theory and the divine right theory

Preparing for Standardized Tests

Have students read the passages under *Individual Freedom* on p. 20 and then complete the sentence below.

Individual freedom in a democracy can best be described as

A absolute.

B threatened by anarchy.

C balanced by societal and governmental rules.

D secondary to the rights of society.

© Pearson Education, Inc.

Preparing for Standardized Tests

Have students read the Primary Sources passages from the English Bill of Rights on p. 30 and then answer the question below.

Based on these passages, what was Parliament's primary concern in writing this document?

A To limit the power of the monarchy.

B To keep the king from pretending things.

C To transfer all power from the monarchy to Parliament.

D To make petitioning illegal.

Preparing for Standardized Tests

Have students read the passages under *Growing Colonial Unity* on pp. 35–36 and then answer the question below.

What is the best explanation for why early attempts at colonial cooperation failed?

A No one put forth a formal plan.

B The British Board of Trade prevented colonists from proposing plans.

C Colonists were content with the government as it was.

D Colonists still considered themselves British subjects, and did not feel particular loyalty to the other colonies.

Preparing for Standardized Tests

Have students read the passages under *The Virginia Plan* on p. 50 and then complete the sentence below.

From the passages, you can infer that smaller States might have found the Virginia Plan too radical because

A it thoroughly rejected the Articles.

B by basing representation in the houses on population or monetary support, it favored the larger States.

C it did not call for an executive branch.

D it did not provide for a national judiciary.

© Pearson Education, Inc.

Preparing for Standardized Tests
Chapter 3

Preparing for Standardized Tests

Have students read the Primary Sources selection from *The Federalist* on p. 67 and then complete the sentence below.

From the passage, you can infer that Madison believed tyranny

A results when power is held equally by many groups.

B could not happen in a democracy.

C is a result of having a strong executive branch.

D is a danger when powers are not separated among the branches of government.

© Pearson Education, Inc.

Preparing for Standardized Tests

Have students read the passages under *The Powers of the National Government* on pp. 89–91 and then answer the question below.

Which of the following is *not* a power of the National Government?

A raising and maintaining armed forces

B granting patents and copyrights

C enacting uniform marriage and divorce laws

D prohibiting racial discrimination in access to such places as restaurants and hotels

Preparing for Standardized Tests

Have students read the passages under *Admitting New States* on pp. 99–100 and then answer the question below.

What would be the main obstacle to an area achieving Statehood?

A the failure of the President to sign an act of admission

B not receiving an enabling act from Congress

C not meeting certain requirements set by Congress

D opposition by the American people

© Pearson Education, Inc.

Preparing for Standardized Tests
Chapter 5

Preparing for Standardized Tests

Have students read the passages under *The American Ideological Consensus* on pp. 121–122 and then answer the question below.

Which sentence best describes consensus in the United States?

A Americans generally agree on basic political issues.

B Sharp political divisions in the nation make consensus difficult.

C All Americans hold the same political views.

D Consensus has produced two major parties that are exactly alike.

Preparing for Standardized Tests

Have students read the passages under *The Era of the Democrats, 1800–1860* on pp. 127–128 and then answer the question below.

From the passages, what can you infer was the main reason that Democrats had lost power by the end of this era?

A The Whigs were undefeatable.

B Because of so many factions, the Democratic party had become fragmented.

C The Civil War caused disunity.

D President Jackson was not reelected.

© Pearson Education, Inc.

Preparing for Standardized Tests

Have students read the passages under *Other Qualifications* on pp. 154–156 and then answer the question below.

Which of the following is still a valid voting requirement in most States today?

A passing a literacy test

B registering

C paying a poll tax

D being a white male

Preparing for Standardized Tests

Have students read the passages under *Factors Affecting Turnout* on p. 166 and then answer the question below.

Which of the following is described in the text as the main reason why people fail to vote?

A bad weather

B "time-zone fallout"

C lack of interest

D cumbersome election procedures

Preparing for Standardized Tests

Have students read the passages under *The Fifteenth Amendment* on pp. 159–160 and then answer the question below.

Why was the 15th Amendment ineffective for decades in ensuring the right of African Americans to vote?

A Congress did nothing to enforce it.

B Its wording was unclear and confusing.

C African Americans did not exercise their right to vote.

D Supreme Court decisions weakened the amendment.

© Pearson Education, Inc.

Preparing for Standardized Tests
Chapter 7

Preparing for Standardized Tests

Have students read the passages under *Precincts and Polling Places* on p. 190 and then answer the question below.

Which of the following would NOT be a polling place?

A a school

B a county

C a church

D a recreation center

Preparing for Standardized Tests

Have students read the passages under *Loopholes in the Law* on pp. 201–202 and then complete the sentence below.

Money spent by a group to sponsor a State Republican voter awareness campaign for young people would be considered

A hard money.

B independent campaign spending.

C an issue ad.

D soft money.

© Pearson Education, Inc.

Preparing for Standardized Tests

Have students read the passages under *Family and Education* on pp. 209–211 and then complete the sentence below.

"Political socialization" can be defined as

A the process by which each person acquires political opinions.

B the choosing of a political party.

C allegiance to a family or school.

D learning how to be a politician.

Preparing for Standardized Tests

Have students read the passages under *Newspapers* on pp. 225–226 and then answer the question below.

What is the main reason for the decline in the number of newspapers published?

A People are not interested in local papers.

B Newspapers are too political.

C Newspapers only express one point of view.

D Newspapers must compete with television and other media.

© Pearson Education, Inc.

Preparing for Standardized Tests
Chapter 9

Preparing for Standardized Tests

Have students read the Primary Sources quotation on p. 238 and then answer the question below.

What is the best synonym for the term *adverse to* in this passage?

A angry with

B opposed to

C contented with

D in agreement with

Preparing for Standardized Tests

Have students read the passages under *Lobbyists at Work* on pp. 252–254 and then answer the question below.

Which of the following techniques would *not* be used by a lobbyist today?

A disseminating reports to policymakers

B organizing grass roots campaigns

C testifying at hearings

D offering gifts to influential members of Congress

© Pearson Education, Inc.

Preparing for Standardized Tests

Have students read the passages under *Congressional Elections* on pp. 269–272 and then complete the sentence below.

Off-year elections are

A congressional elections held in odd-numbered years.

B congressional elections that occur in the nonpresidential years.

C elections for both President and Congress.

D congressional elections held on different years in different States.

Preparing for Standardized Tests

Have students read the Primary Sources quotation by Rep. Luther Patrick on p. 282 and then answer the following question.

What is the *main* point of this passage?

A Members of Congress must play many roles.

B Members of Congress owe their primary responsibility to the demands of the public.

C Members of Congress must be experienced in many different fields.

D Members of Congress are so busy dealing with public requests that they don't have time for their primary roles as legislators.

© Pearson Education, Inc.

Preparing for Standardized Tests
Chapter 11

Preparing for Standardized Tests

Have students read the passages under *The Power to Tax* on pp. 294–296 and then answer the question below.

What is a protective tariff?

A a low tax on imported goods to encourage their purchase by Americans

B a tax on exports

C a tax on cigarettes to make them more expensive and thus protect the public from the health risks of smoking

D a tax on imported goods to increase their price and make them less popular than American goods

---

Preparing for Standardized Tests

Have students read the passages under *Richard Nixon* on pp. 312–313 and then answer the question below.

Which of the following was the first event in the chain of events leading to impeachment proceedings against Nixon?

A investigations by the Senate Watergate Committee

B the reporting by the *Washington Post* of the Democratic national headquarters break-in

C Nixon's resignation

D the subpoena of Nixon by the House Judiciary Committee

© Pearson Education, Inc.

Preparing for Standardized Tests

Chapter 12

Preparing for Standardized Tests

Have students read the passages under *The President of the Senate* on pp. 323–324 and then complete the sentence below.

From the passages, you can infer that a Vice President will have more influence as president of the Senate if

A he or she is a powerful orator.

B he or she has a good relationship with the president *pro tempore*.

C he or she is from the same party as the majority party of the Senate.

D the Speaker of the House is not popular.

Preparing for Standardized Tests

Have students read the passages under *Rules* on p. 338 and then answer the question below.

What *main* purpose does the complex system of House rules serve?

A It makes representatives pay more attention to congressional proceedings.

B It helps ensure that as many bills as possible are passed.

C It helps members of the House manage their schedules better.

D It provides a way for the public to follow congressional hearings.

Preparing for Standardized Tests

Have students read the passages under *Conference Committees* on pp. 344–346 and then answer the question below.

Which statement best expresses the constitutional reason for conference committees in Congress?

A The Constitution requires such committees.

B The Constitution requires that both houses of Congress pass bills in identical form.

C The Constitution requires members of both houses to consult each other on issues of national concern.

D The Constitution requires that the President participate in committees.

© Pearson Education, Inc.

Preparing for Standardized Tests
Chapter 13

Preparing for Standardized Tests

Have students read the quotations by John Nance Garner and Alben Barkley on p. 362, and then answer the question below.

What do you think is these writers' main point about the vice presidency?

A All Vice Presidents are incompetent.

B Vice Presidents do not have the ability that Presidents have.

C The office of the vice presidency places few demands on the person who fills it.

D Vice Presidents are not usually ambitious.

Preparing for Standardized Tests

Have students read the passages under *Primaries Today* on p. 370 and then answer the question below.

What factor has increased the significance of money and name recognition in presidential primaries?

A front-loading

B State laws

C the New Hampshire primary

D the policies of the Democratic National Convention

Preparing for Standardized Tests

Have students read the passages under *Proposed Reforms* on pp. 382–384 and then answer the question below.

Which plan might encourage gerrymandering?

A the district plan

B the national bonus plan

C the proportional plan

D the direct popular election plan

© Pearson Education, Inc.

Preparing for Standardized Tests

Have students read the passages under *Commander in Chief* on pp. 401–403 and then complete the sentence below.

From the passages, you can infer that

A the presidential role of commander in chief is purely a symbolic one.

B Presidents always delegate military power to subordinates.

C the President and Congress share equal power concerning the armed forces.

D Presidents have various means of using the commander in chief role to carry out their goals.

© Pearson Education, Inc.

Preparing for Standardized Tests
Chapter 15

Preparing for Standardized Tests

Have students read the passages under *The Name Game* on pp. 416–418 and then answer the question below.

Which of the following titles may only be used in association with agencies of Cabinet rank?

A department

B bureau

C corporation

D authority

Preparing for Standardized Tests

Have students read the passages under *The Cabinet* on pp. 426–429 and then complete the sentence below.

According to the passages, the Cabinet is mandated by

A the Constitution.

B tradition.

C an act of Congress.

D individual Presidents.

© Pearson Education, Inc.

Preparing for Standardized Tests

Have students read the passages under *The Implied Limitation* on pp. 448–449 and then answer the question below.

Which of the following State activities would have federal taxes imposed on it?

A the selling of liquor

B providing a police force

C running public hospitals

D building bridges

Preparing for Standardized Tests

Have students read the passages under *Controllable and Uncontrollable Spending* on pp. 459–461 and then answer the question below.

Which of the following is an example of controllable spending?

A paying interest on the national debt

B food stamps

C aid to education

D welfare payments

© Pearson Education, Inc.

Preparing for Standardized Tests
Chapter 17

Preparing for Standardized Tests

Have students read the passages under *The Good Neighbor Policy* on p. 483 and then answer the question below.

From the passages, what can you infer that the phrase "dollar diplomacy" means?

A forcing a country to use the dollar as its national currency

B providing foreign aid to a country

C the use of economic policy to protect a country's business interests

D forming an economic alliance

Preparing for Standardized Tests

Have students read the Primary Sources quotation on pp. 492–493 and then answer the question below.

What is the best definition for the word *proactively* in this selection?

A completely

B strongly

C in the future

D in advance

© Pearson Education, Inc.

Preparing for Standardized Tests

Have students read the passages under *Supreme Court Jurisdiction* on pp. 519–520 and then answer the question below.

What jurisdiction does the Supreme Court have?

A appellate jurisdiction

B original jurisdiction

C original and appellate jurisdiction

D any case it chooses to take

© Pearson Education, Inc.

Preparing for Standardized Tests
Chapter 19

Preparing for Standardized Tests

Have students read the Primary Sources quotation by Hugo Black on p. 539 and then answer the question below.

What is the *main* point of this passage?

A The Constitution prohibits laws respecting an establishment of religion.

B It is not the government's place to compose official prayers.

C Religious programs may only be carried out by the government.

D Americans want the right to recite religious prayers.

Preparing for Standardized Tests

Have students read the passages under *Private Property* on pp. 557–558 and then answer the question below.

Which of the following statements is most accurate?

A It is unconstitutional to petition in a shopping mall.

B All States prohibit petitioning at a shopping mall.

C Owners of shopping malls may allow petitioners on a case-by-case basis.

D Whether people can petition at a shopping mall depends on each State's constitution.

© Pearson Education, Inc.

Preparing for Standardized Tests
Chapter 20

Preparing for Standardized Tests

Have students read the passages under *The Exclusionary Rule* on pp. 573–574 and then complete the sentence below.

The main point of the exclusionary rule is to

A protect people's private possessions.

B prevent police misconduct.

C lessen States' caseloads by limiting the use of evidence.

D keep police from searching homes for evidence.

Preparing for Standardized Tests

Have students read the passages under *Treason* on p. 588 and then answer the question below.

What is the only crime explicitly defined in the Constitution?

A treason

B murder

C killing a police officer

D committing rape

© Pearson Education, Inc.

Preparing for Standardized Tests
Chapter 21

Preparing for Standardized Tests

Have students read the passages under *Classification by Sex* on pp. 605–606 and then answer the question below.

Which of the following would be a valid reason for upholding a law that treats men and women differently?

A Gender discrimination is not unconstitutional.

B Men and women are fundamentally different.

C The law serves a specific governmental objective.

D The Constitution does not mention sex.

Preparing for Standardized Tests

Have students read the passages under *Deportation* on p. 617 and then answer the question below.

Which of the following would *not* be a reason for deporting an alien?

A holding a minimum-wage job

B illegal entry

C conviction of a federal crime

D conviction of a State crime

© Pearson Education, Inc.

Preparing for Standardized Tests

Have students read the passages under *The Cabinet* on p. 629 and then answer the question below.

What is the *main* importance of the shadow cabinet?

A It acts as a "watchdog" on the party in power.

B It keeps the opposition party informed on important issues.

C It provides opposing points of view.

D It is ready to run the government should an opposition party gain power.

Preparing for Standardized Tests

Have students read the passages under *Political Parties* on pp. 636–637 and then complete the sentence below.

Though Japan has a multiparty system, Japanese politics

A are usually dominated by one party.

B are usually dominated by two parties.

C do not allow for splinter parties.

D restrict the activities of unpopular parties.

© Pearson Education, Inc.

Preparing for Standardized Tests
Chapter 23

Preparing for Standardized Tests

Have students read the passages under *Socialism in Developing Countries* on p. 669 and then answer the question below.

Which of the following is *not* a reason that developing countries adopt socialism?

A It gives people more say in government.

B It allows leaders to win broad public support.

C It encourages the growth of key industries.

D It enables leaders to channel investments easily.

Preparing for Standardized Tests

Have students read the passages under *Characteristics of Communist Economies* on pp. 673–674 and then answer the question below.

Which statement most accurately describes the role of the Communist Party?

A It influences government decisions.

B It is part of the government.

C For all purposes, it is synonymous with the state.

D Its influence depends on who heads it.

© Pearson Education, Inc.

Preparing for Standardized Tests

Have students read the chart titled "How to Propose Changes to a State Constitution" on p. 687 and then answer the question below.

Who has been responsible for writing and revising most State constitutions?

A the voters

B the legislature

C the governor

D conventions

Preparing for Standardized Tests

Have students read the passages under *The Governorship* on p. 694 and then answer the question below.

In the first State constitutions, most government powers were given to

A the governors.

B the voters.

C the legislatures.

D special interest groups.

© Pearson Education, Inc.

Preparing for Standardized Tests
Chapter 25

Preparing for Standardized Tests

Have students read the passages under *The Mayor-Council Form* on p. 726 and then answer the question below.

Which of the following is NOT a criticism of the strong-mayor government?

A It relies on the capacities of the mayor.

B Mayor-council disputes can stall government.

C The mayor has strong leadership in running city affairs.

D It is complicated and hard to understand.

Preparing for Standardized Tests

Have students read the passages under *Nontax Sources* on p. 743 and then answer the question below.

Which of the following would NOT be a nontax source?

A taxes on admission to movie theaters

B tolls on roads and bridges

C court fines

D state-run lotteries

© Pearson Education, Inc.

Preparing for Standardized Tests
Answer Key

CHAPTER 1, P. 30

D

C

CHAPTER 2, P. 31

A

D

B

CHAPTER 3, P. 32

D

CHAPTER 4, P. 33

C

A

CHAPTER 5, P. 34

A

B

CHAPTER 6, P. 35

B

C

A

CHAPTER 7, P. 36

B

D

CHAPTER 8, P. 37

A

D

CHAPTER 9, P. 38

B

D

CHAPTER 10, P. 39

A

D

CHAPTER 11, P. 40

D

B

CHAPTER 12, P. 41

C

C

B

CHAPTER 13, P. 42

C

A

A

CHAPTER 14, P. 43

D

CHAPTER 15, P. 44

A

B

CHAPTER 16, P. 45

A

C

© Pearson Education, Inc.

Preparing for Standardized Tests
Answer Key (continued)

CHAPTER 17, P. 46

   C

   D

CHAPTER 18, P. 47

   C

CHAPTER 19, P. 48

   B

   D

CHAPTER 20, P. 49

   B

   A

CHAPTER 21, P. 50

   C

   A

CHAPTER 22, P. 51

   D

   A

CHAPTER 23, P. 52

   A

   C

CHAPTER 24, P. 53

   D

   C

CHAPTER 25, P. 54

   C

   A

© Pearson Education, Inc.